Specimen Sight-Reading Tests for Horn

Grades 6–8

ABRSM
Printed on materials from sustainable sources

6.50

1

Allegro
p
p
cresc.
f

2

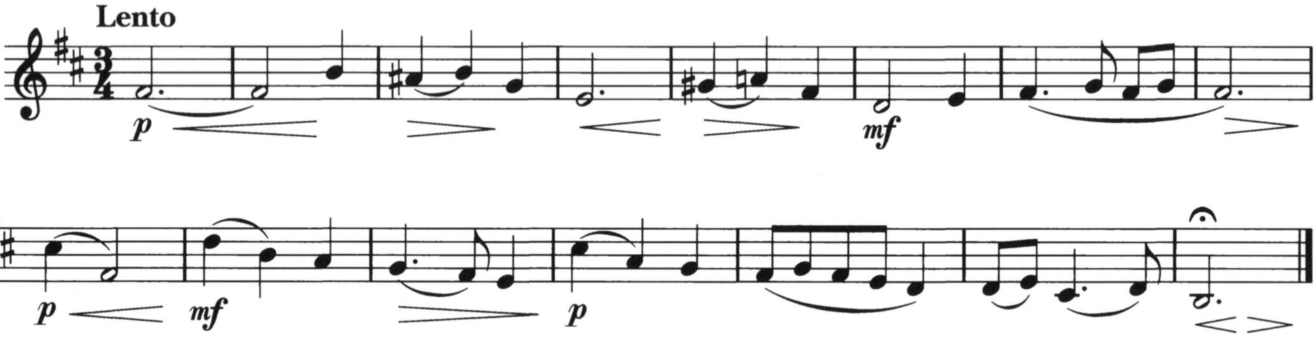
Lento
p
mf
p
mf
p

3

Giocoso
mp
f
p
f
p

4

Andante
p
f
p
f
p

Alla marcia

5 

Allegro

6 

Ritmico

7 

Lento

8 

9
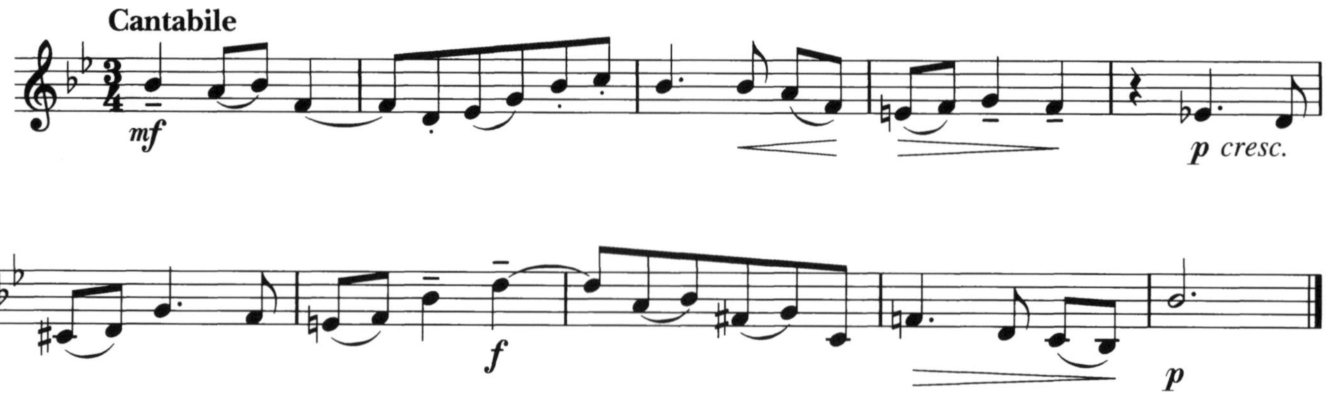
Cantabile
p cresc.

10
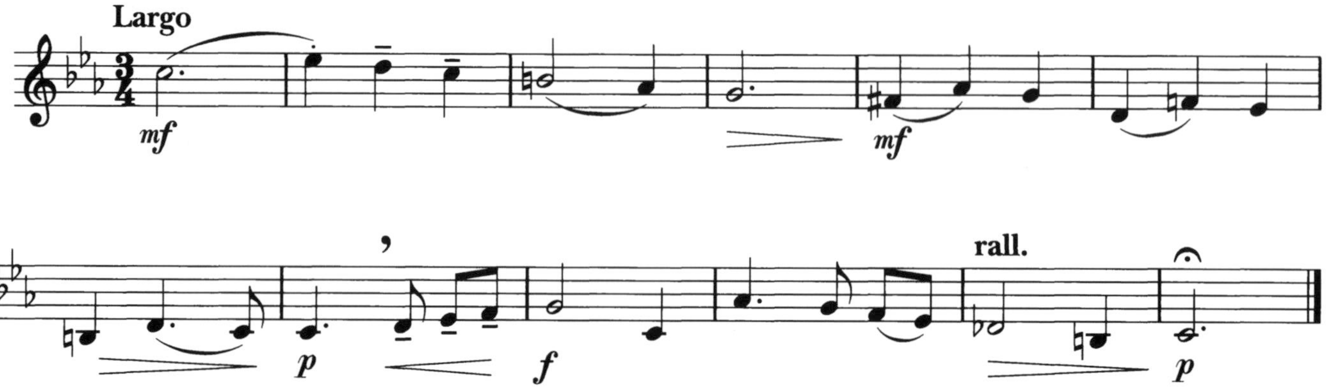
Largo
rall.

11
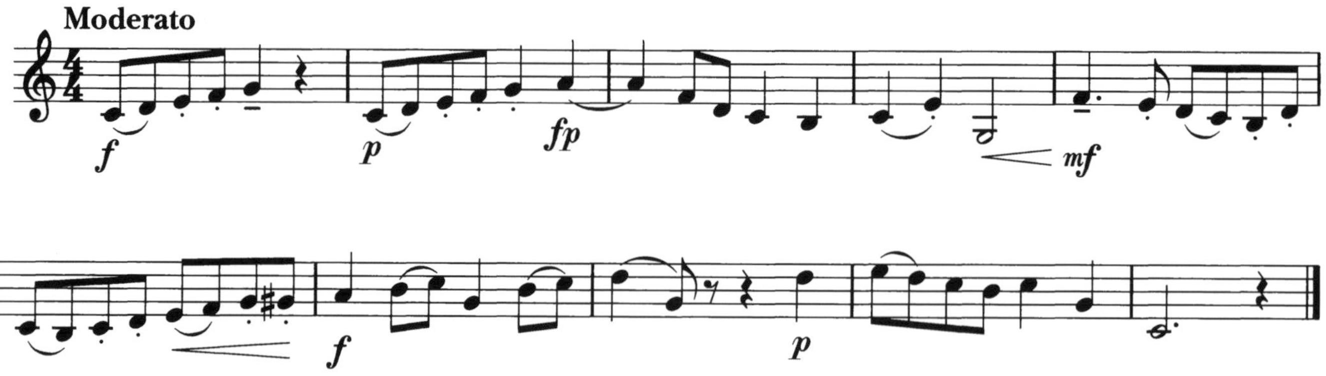
Moderato

12
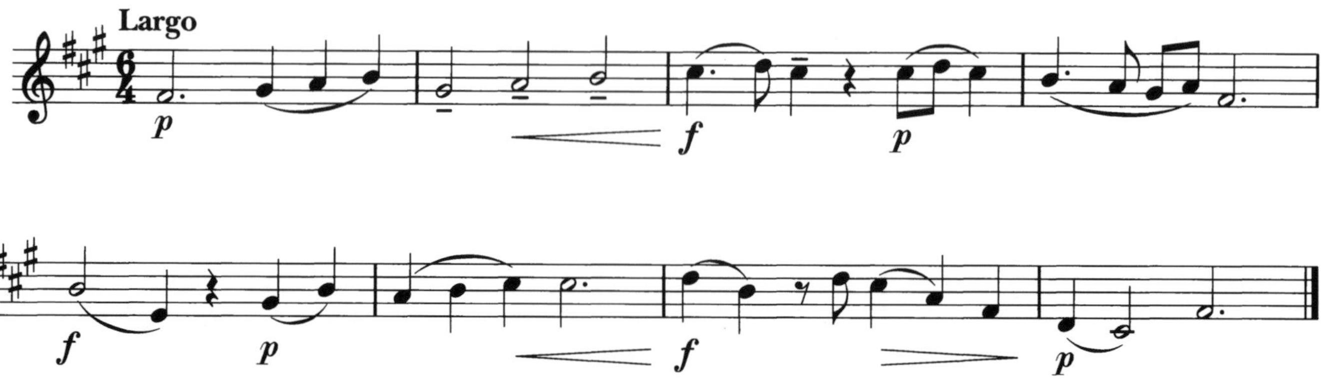
Largo

Maestoso

13

Allegretto

14

Vivo

15

Doloroso

16

17

18

19

20

1
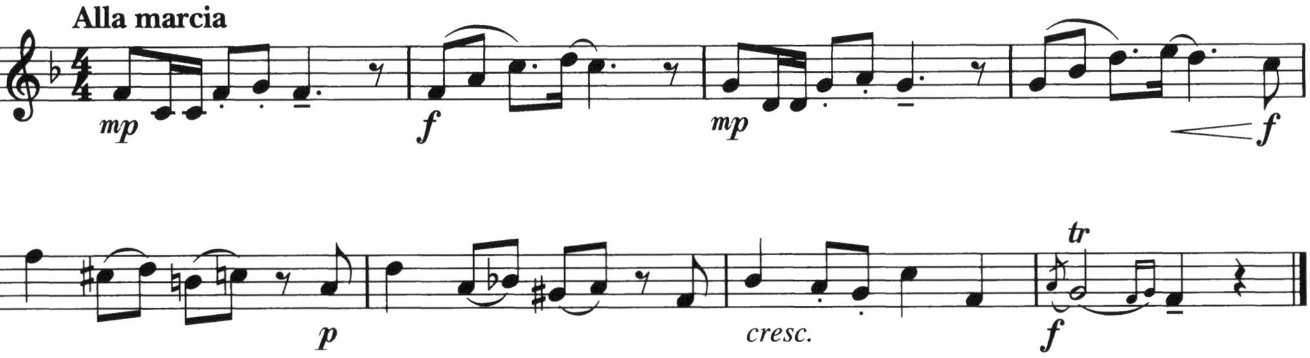
Alla marcia
cresc.

2
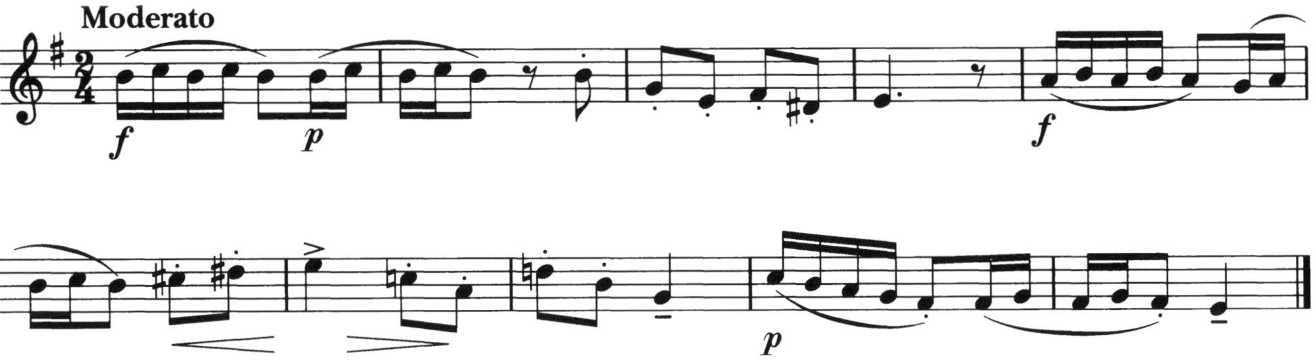
Moderato

3
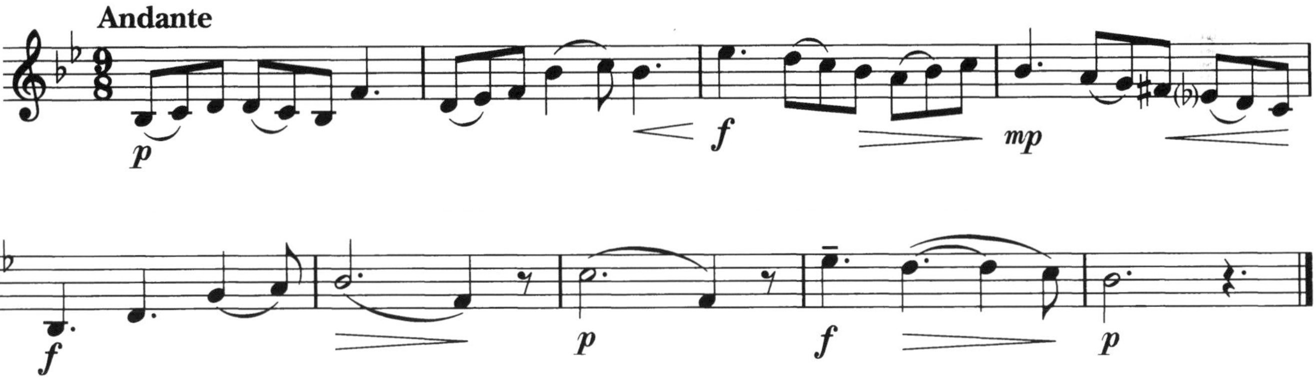
Andante

4
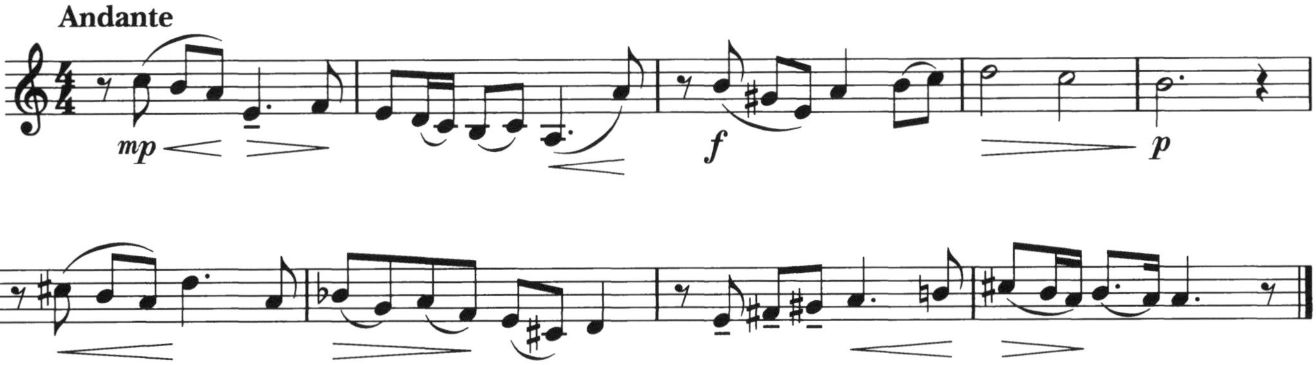
Andante

5

6

7

8

9 **Alla marcia**

10 **Ritmico**

11 **Moderato**

12 **Andante**

13

Moderato
mp
mf
mp
f
dim.
p

14

Giocoso
mf
f
p
mf
p

15

Grazioso
mf
p
f
p

16

Moderato
f
p
mf
p

17

Moderato

18

Andante

19

Moderato

20

Vigoroso
rall.
a tempo
cresc.

1
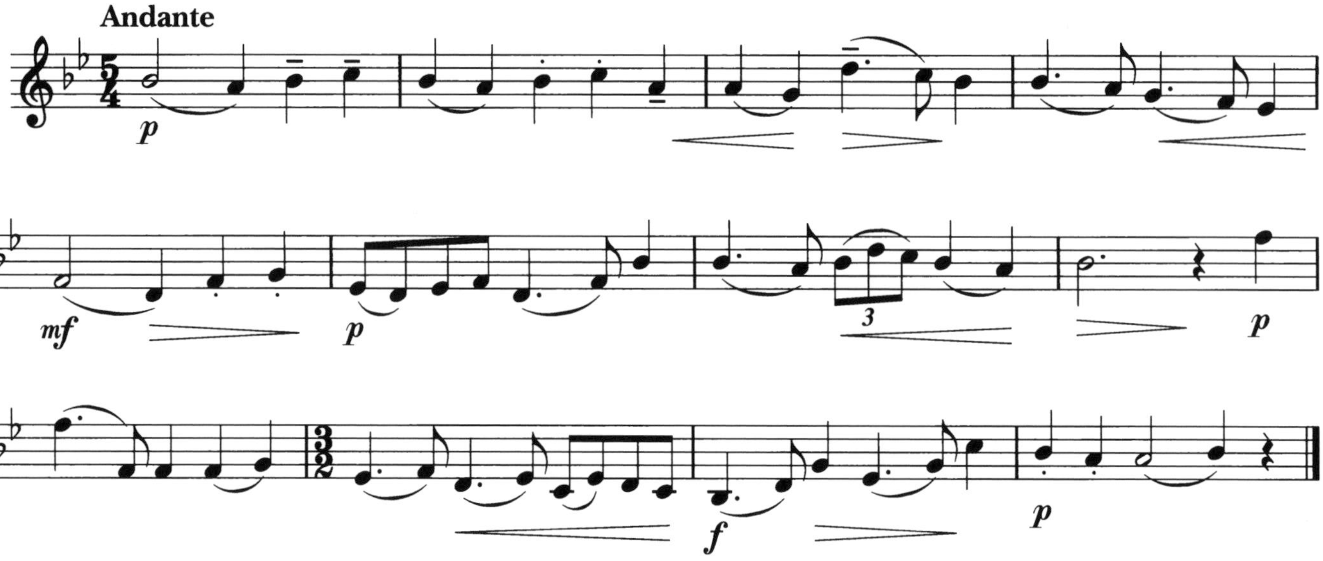
Andante

2
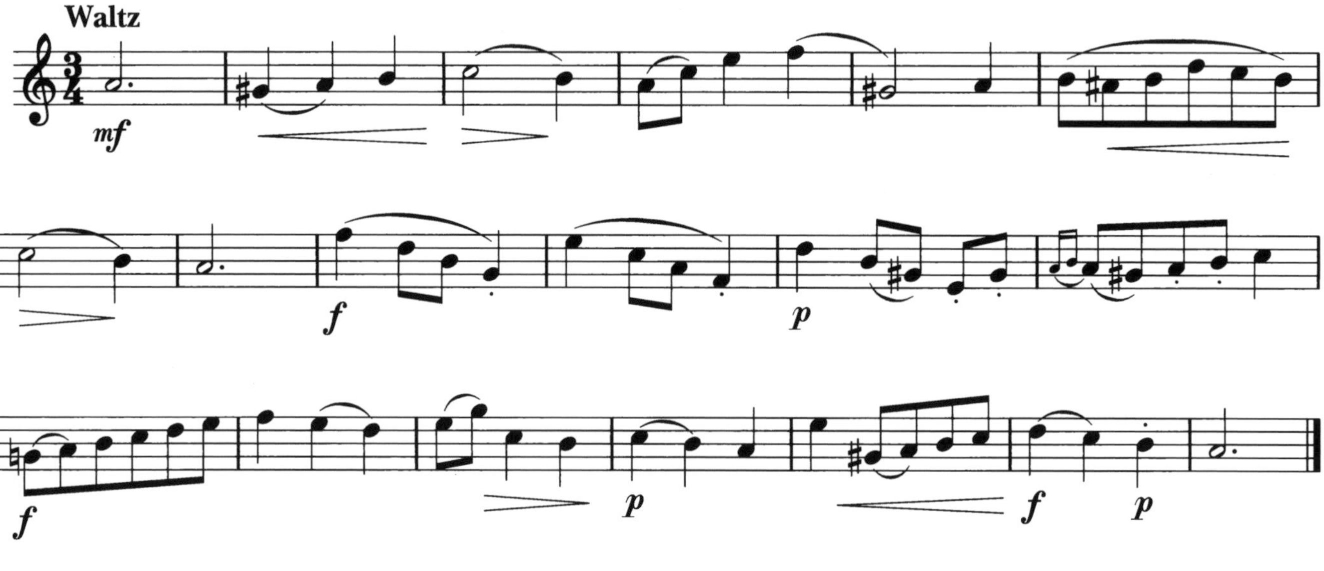
Waltz

3
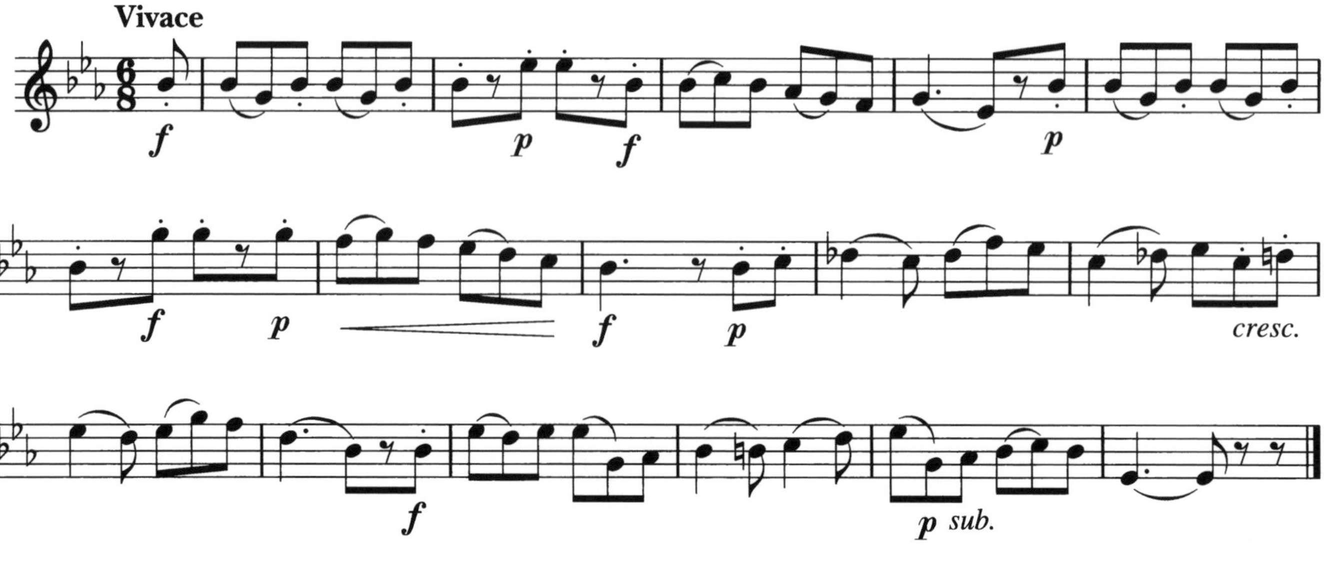
Vivace
cresc.
p sub.

Lento

4

Moderato

5

Ritmico

6

7
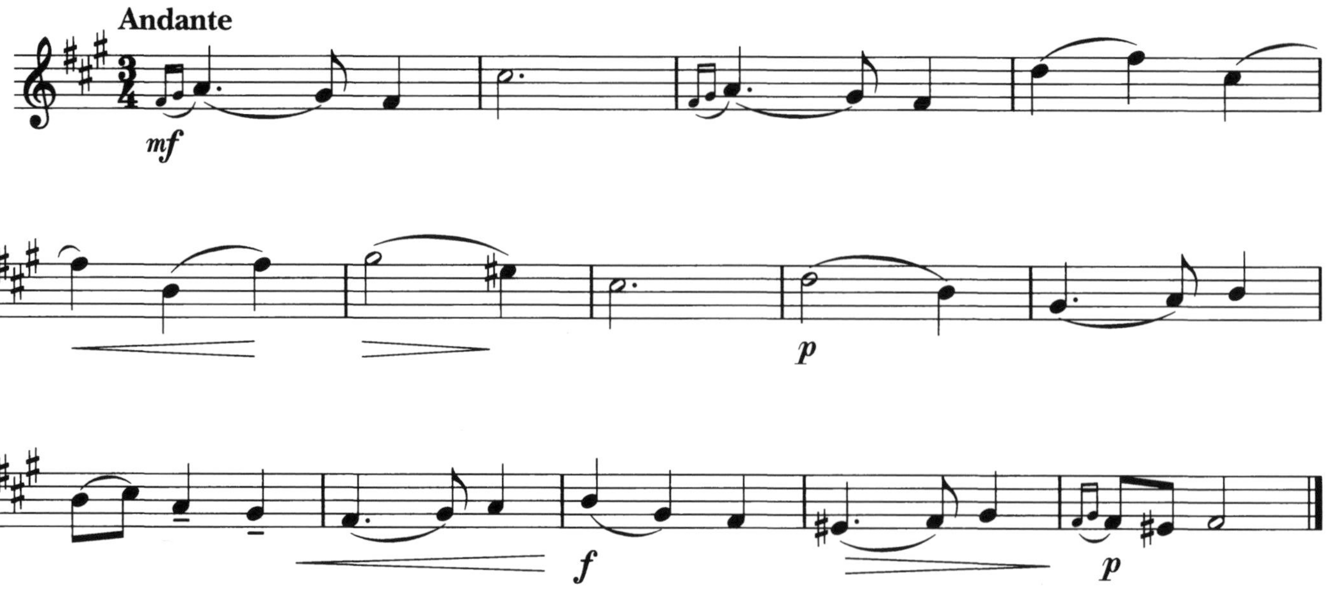
Andante
mf
p
f
p

8
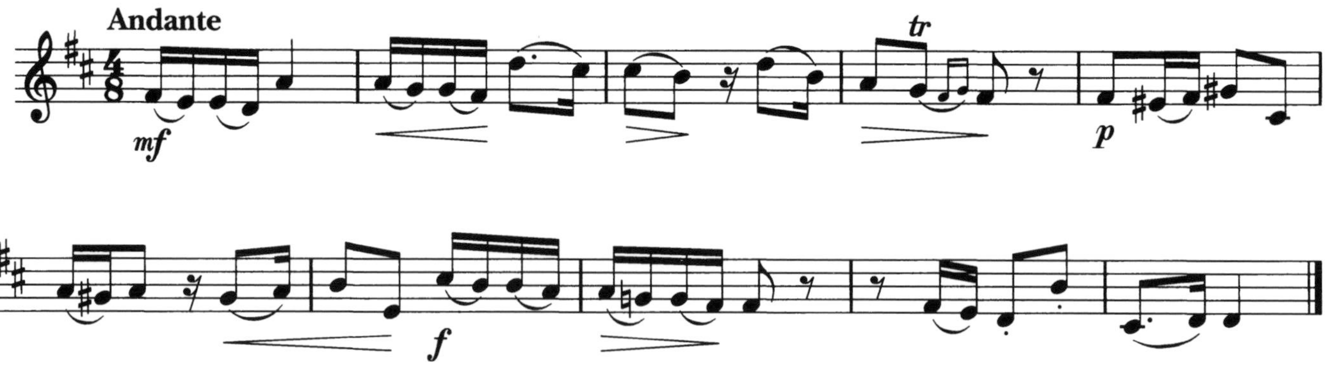
Andante
mf
tr
p
f

9
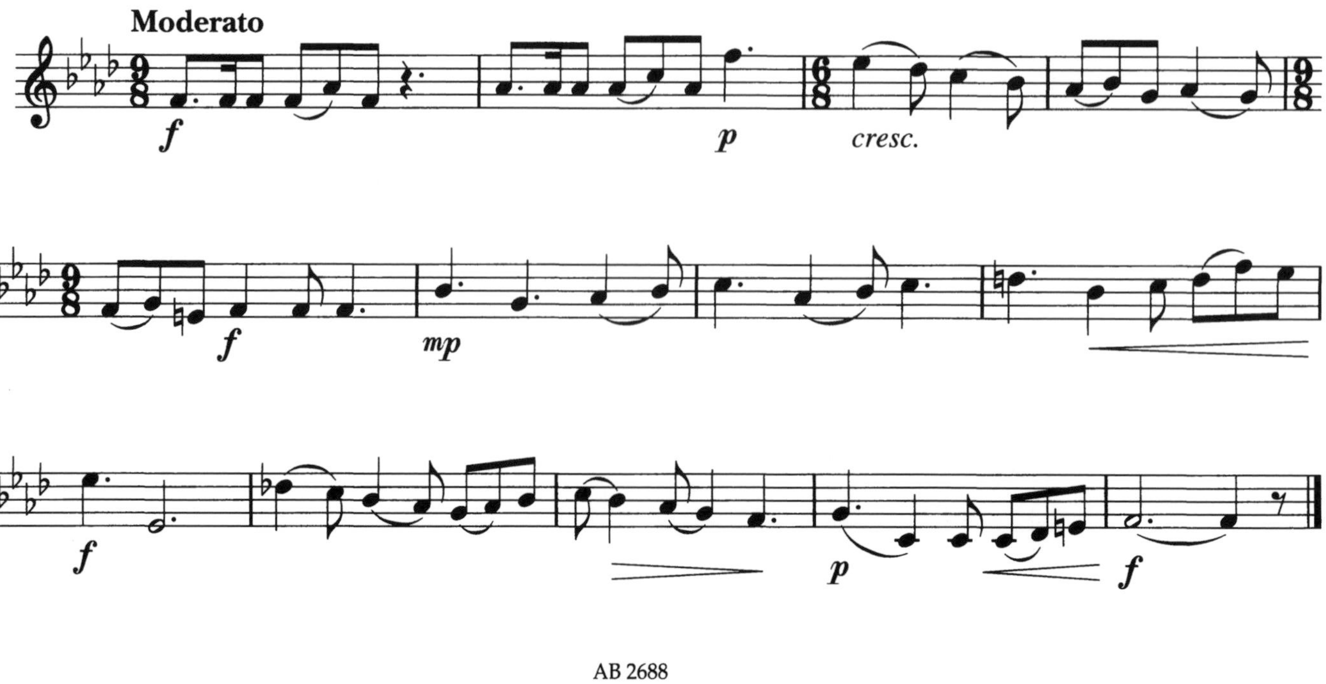
Moderato
f
p
cresc.
f
mp
f
p
f

10 Lento

11 Moderato

12 Allegro

13 Allegro

14 Vivo

15 Vivo

AB 2688

Printed and bound in Great Britain by Caligraving Limited

02:16